Fisher Educational Ltd

Fisher Educational Ltd is a company devoted to improving mathematics and learning through its websites 10Tickers.com, 10Ticks.co.uk, 10Ticks.co.za, 10Ticks.com.au, 10Ticks.com.my, 10Ticks.com and BoffinSquad.co.uk.

10Ticks, 10Tickers and BoffinSquad are registered trade marks of Fisher Educational Ltd in the UK and in certain other countries.

© **Fisher Educational Ltd 2020**

Words by Jik, Jean Fisher and Ian Fisher, a mother and son writing team.

Illustrations by Emma Knowles
www.cartoonillustration.co.uk

The moral rights of the author have been asserted.
First published 2020.

10 9 8 7 6 5 4 3 2 1

British Library Cataloguing in Publication Data.

A catalogue record for this book is available from the British Library.

ISBN: 978-1-912492-01-5

How to use this book

The experiences and activities contained within this book are intended to enable your child to develop confidently, learn effectively and become ready for school.

Numeracy and reading concepts are introduced sequentially and progressively. They go hand in hand with play experiences and are not intended to replace these valuable, first-hand play experiences of early learning.

Use the books in short, regular, frequent sessions (until your child's interest wanes), rather than occasional, lengthy ones.

When necessary, help your child to read these books and understand the mathematics and reading involved. Draw attention to the difference between each number and each letter and their names. Use the flash cards at the back of each book to help you. When ready, teach the correct formation of letters and numbers.

From the outset, when your child is interested, teach the correct way to hold a tool, (i.e. pencil, crayon, paintbrush and scissors).

Help him/her to trace some of the simple pictures.

Draw letters and numbers in sand or in the air. Use plasticine to make letters and numbers.

There are free worksheets you can use with your child if you register at www.10Tickers.com.

Some jingles and rhymes are intended for you to chant and/or dance with him/her, so that he/she feels the rhythm and beat involved. Enjoy the movement and sing/dance together.

Reinforce these learning tasks and extend the relevant vocabulary by using articles from newspapers, comics, magazines and everyday objects.

As a bonus feature, find the hidden QR codes. These codes lead to online games and activities. The one below gives an extended version of these notes. A suitable tablet device and an internet connection are required.

Ticker 2

Hello.
I am
Ticker 2.

2   2   2

I am blue.

I have a name.
It is
Ticker Two.

Two.
Two.
Two.

I have **2** eyes.
I have **2** arms.
I have **2** legs.

Find my **2** eyes.
Find my **2** arms.
Find my **2** legs.

I am a little Ticker,
all in blue.

Another Ticker comes to play.
Now there are 2.

Play time.
Oh what fun!

Ticker 1 and Ticker 2 play in the garden.
It is light and sunny.

Ticker 1 and Ticker 2
play on the see-saw.

Up, down, up, down.

Up, up, up.
Down, down, down.

Ticker 1 goes up.

Ticker 2 goes down.

Ticker 1 and Ticker 2 sit down.
They have a rest.

They sit in the garden with the **black** cat.

Look at the big house.

Look at the big garden.

One big house.

One big garden.

What can you see?

Bushes and flowers

and a little bumble bee.

Can you find

2 **red** flowers,

2 **blue** flowers,

2 **yellow** flowers

and 1 little bumble bee?

Ticker 1 goes **inside** the big house.

Ticker 2 is **outside**. He is in the big garden.

14

It is night time.
Outside it is dark.

It is time for Ticker 2 to go inside the house.

Ticker 2 looks out of the window.

He can see 1 big moon in the sky.

He can see lots of stars in the sky.

Look.

I big moon in the sky.

The moon is **yellow**.

Look.

Lots of stars in the sky.

The stars are **white**.

It has been a good day for Ticker 1 and Ticker 2.

They are very happy.

Ticker 2 gets into bed and YAWNS!

Night night everyone.

Sleep tight.

Singing time!

Twinkle, twinkle, little star,
how I wonder what you are.
Up above the world so high,
like a diamond in the sky.
Twinkle, twinkle, little star,
how I wonder what you are.

The End

Books in the series

Ticker 1 book | 1 |

Ticker 2 book | 2 |

Ticker 3 book | 3 |

Ticker 4 book | 4 |

Ticker 5 book | 5 |

Ticker 6 book | 6 |

Ticker 7 book | 7 |

Ticker 8 book | 8 |

Ticker 9 book | 9 |

Ticker 10 book | 10 |

Ticker 0 book | 0 |

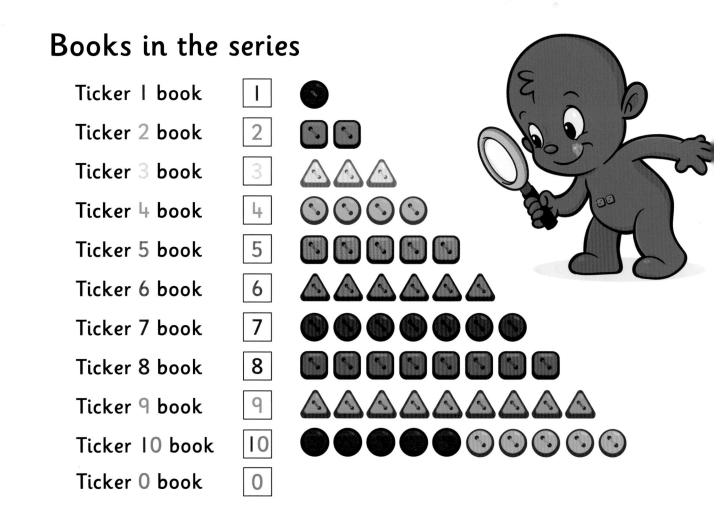